ANGRY BIRDS ™

Giant Coloring and Activity Book

Feathers Will Fly!

Modern Publishing
A Division of Kappa Books Publishers, LLC.
Printed in the U.S.A.

FLYING SKY HIGH!

 # SHIFTY SHADOWS

Match the birds to their shadows.

See Answers

DESTROY THE OINKERS!

FEATHERS WILL FLY!

THE EARLY BIRD CATCHES THE PIGS.

ON A MISSION

The birds are trying to track down the pigs. Help them find their way through the maze!

☆ ☆ ☆ ☆ ☆ ☆ ☆

END

START

See Answers

READY, SET, FLINC!

ALL HAIL KING PIG.

SPOT THE DIFFERENCES

Find and circle six differences in the scenes below.

See Answers

BOMBS AWAY!

PREPARE TO
BE DESTROYED!

SEND THOSE
PIGS PACKING.

BIRD IMPOSTER

Circle the bird that looks different from the others.

See Answers

EGGS NEVER
LOOKED SO GOOD!

TWO BIRDS ARE
BETTER THAN ONE.

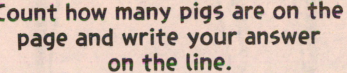

HERE, PIGGY, PIGGY

Count how many pigs are on the
page and write your answer
on the line.

☆ ☆ ☆ ☆ ☆ ☆ ☆

_____

See Answers

YOU CAN RUN,
BUT YOU CAN'T HIDE.

YOU MESSED WITH
THE WRONG BIRD!

6 ANGRY WORDS

How many words can you make out of the word FEATHERS? Write your answers on the lines!

☆ ☆ ☆ ☆ ☆ ☆ ☆

_____

_____

_____

_____

_____

 _____

See Answers

I HOPE WE'RE NOT FORGETTING ANYTHING.

1,2,3...JUMP!

TOOTH OR DARE

How many teeth do the pigs have total? Count them and write your answer on the line!

_____ **See Answers**

CRASH LANDING!

THERE CAN ONLY
BE ONE WINNER.

MISSING PIECE

Can you spot the piece of the puzzle that's missing?
Circle your answer.

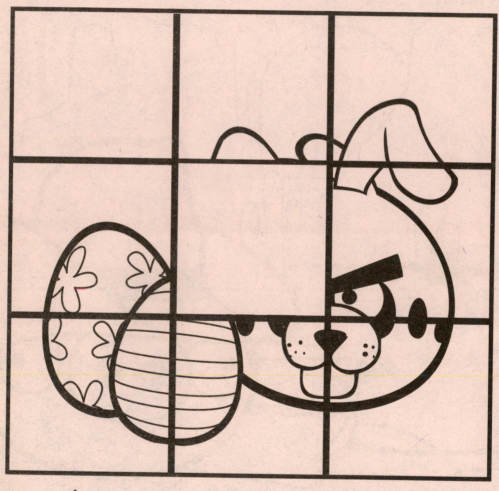

See Answers

THAT'S GOING TO
LEAVE A MARK.

IT'S THE LUCK
OF THE PIG!

THAT'S A BERRY GOOD HIDING PLACE.

IDENTITY CRISIS

This pig needs to look like a bird so he can steal eggs. Dress him up in a bird costume.

☆ ☆ ☆ ☆ ☆ ☆ ☆

CATCH ME IF YOU CAN!

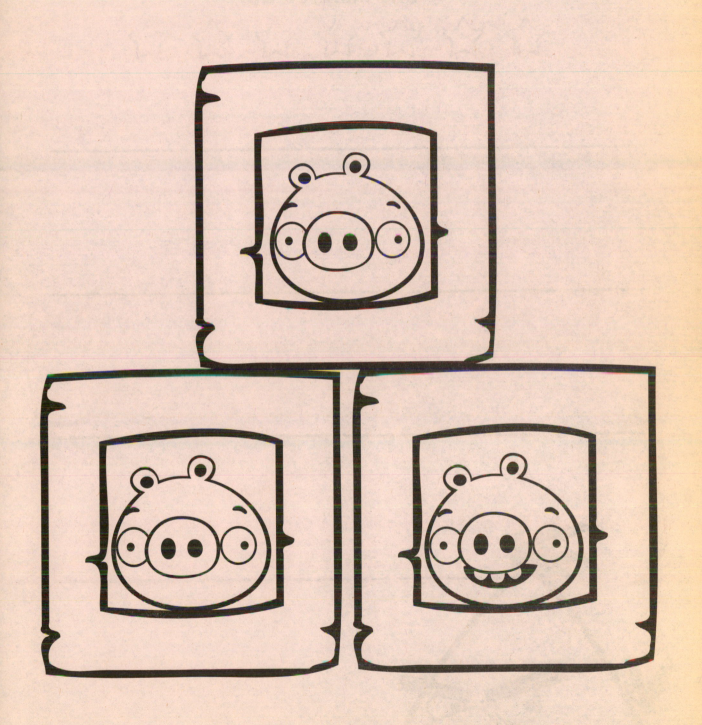

CAN'T KNOCK US DOWN!

 **10**

RHYMING WORDS

How many words can you think of that rhyme with BIRD in under one minute? GO!

☆ ☆ ☆ ☆ ☆ ☆ ☆

_____

_____

_____

_____

See Answers

WHAT A KNOCKOUT!

THIS HAM IS
READY TO HAUNT!

11 CATCH THE CULPRIT

Who is most likely to have stolen the bird's eggs? Circle the thief!

See Answers

RUN AS FAST
AS YOU CAN!

LET'S GET THOSE PIGS!

12

SCENE CREATOR

Create your very own Angry Birds
scene with birds flying high
in the sky trying to knock over
the pigs. Be creative!

☆ ☆ ☆ ☆ ☆ ☆ ☆

HERE I GOOOO!

WATCH WHERE YOU'RE GOING!

BLUEBIRD BUNCH

How many bluebirds are on the page? Write the number on the line.

☆ ☆ ☆ ☆ ☆ ☆ ☆

_____

See Answers

HIDING IN A
WINTER WONDERLAND.

DID SOMEONE FORGET THAT I'M NOT AN EGG?

14

COOL COLORS

What colors are the birds below supposed to be? Color them!

☆ ☆ ☆ ☆ ☆ ☆ ☆

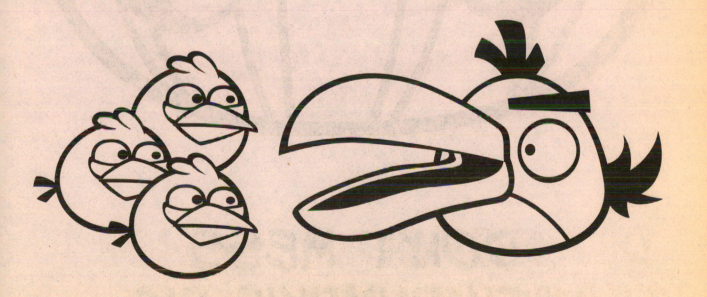

DON'T MESS
WITH PUMPKIN PIE.

I ALMOST GOT AWAY WITH THE EGGS.

I DON'T FEEL
SO GOOD.

COUNTING CRAZE

Circle the group with the most eggs!

See Answers

PIGS ARE SMARTER
THAN YOU THINK.

NO ONE'S SAFE.
NOT EVEN
UNDERGROUND.

I'VE STRUCK JEWELS!

16 MARK OF THE BIRD

Circle the bird with the biggest beak. Underline the bird with the smallest beak. Draw an X over the bird that is red.

See Answers

THESE PIGGIES ARE FEELING THE HEAT!

SOMETHING'S NOT RIGHT.

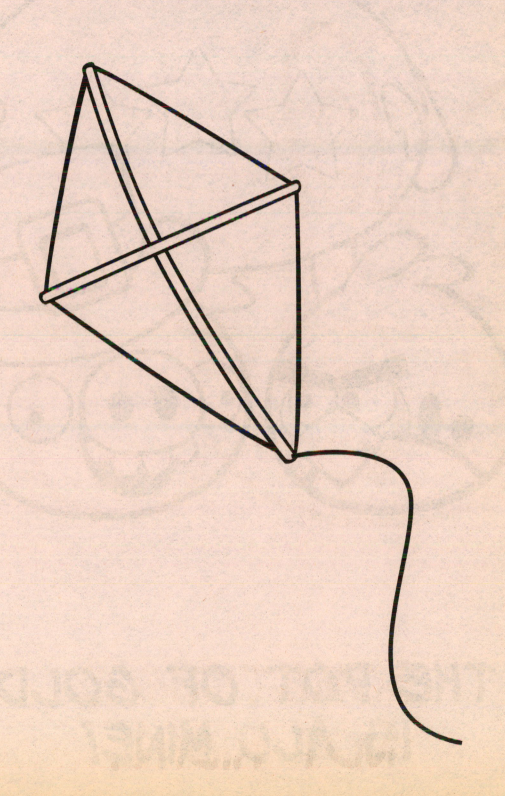

THE POT OF GOLD
IS ALL MINE!

LIVING THE GOOD LIFE

THAT EGG
LOOKS TASTY.

BERRY MADNESS

Can you find the birds hidden in the
mountain of strawberries?
Color them!

See Answers

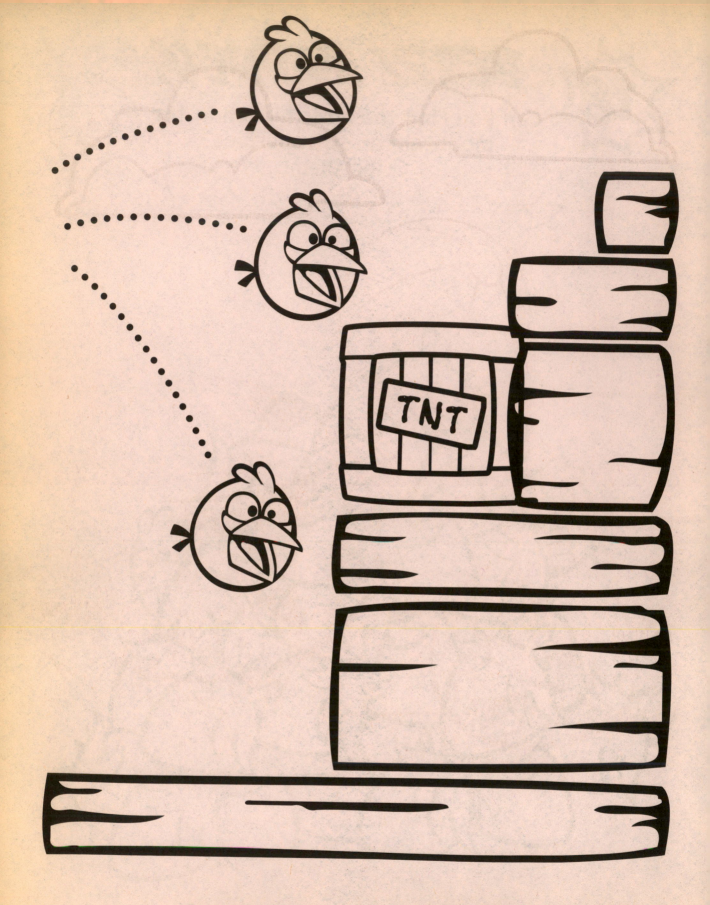

TAKE COVER!

BIRD BREAK

VICTORY WILL
BE OURS!

WORD SEARCH

19

See if you can find all the words listed below in the word search!

☆ ☆ ☆ ☆ ☆ ☆ ☆

Eggs	Pigs
Knockout	Birds
Slingshot	Victory

```
S V E G G S X N I O Y L
B S W V N O P R L G R H
X U L Z C A P G G E O K
T E E I K Z I F B T T N
I N L U N H T D Q F C O
K A T C P G U Y F X I C
P E M R U N S M E S V K
I O B C N C A H L N T O
G N V X M K D S O U X U
S S D R I B D O R T E T
```

See Answers

THIS IS STARTING
TO HURT!

LOVE IS IN THE AIR

I'M FEELING A
LITTLE WOOZY.

RHYME TIME

How many words can you rhyme wtih PIG in less than one minute? GO!

☆ ☆ ☆ ☆ ☆ ☆ ☆

_____

_____

_____

_____

_____

_____

See Answers

RESCUE THE EGGS!

WHAT AN
EGG-CELLENT SIGHT!

NAME GAME

Can you name the color of these birds just by looking at them from behind? Write their names on the lines below them.

_____   _____   _____

_____   _____   _____

See Answers

MISSION: PIG-POSSIBLE!

EG T-CELLENT MAZE!

CHIRP IF YOU'RE GREEN!

22

EGG-CELLENT MAZE!

Help these birds find the correct
path through the maze to get
to their eggs.

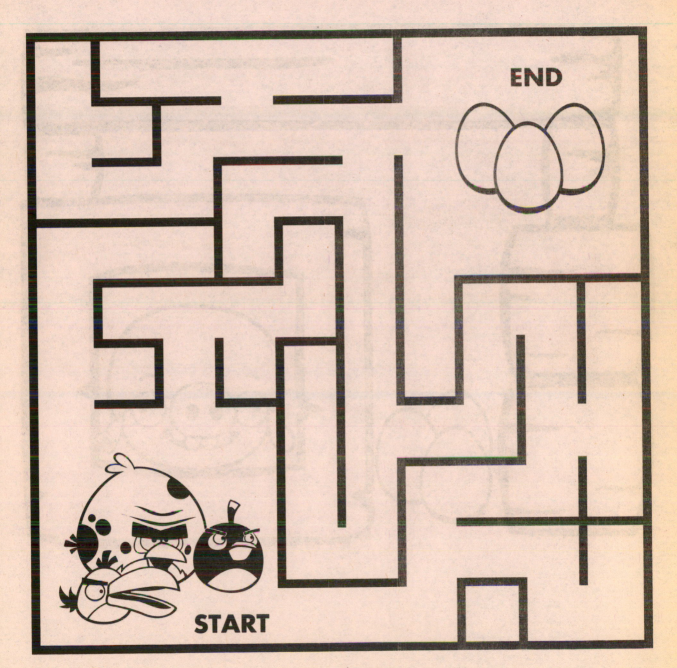

END

START

See Answers

SAFETY FIRST!

DID WE HEAR AN "OINK"?

OH, MY BIRD

What would you look like if YOU were an Angry Bird? Draw yourself!

THE EGGS ARE MISSING!

SMALL PIG IN
A BIG CITY.

24 COLOR BY NUMBER

Using the code, color the scene below!

☆ ☆ ☆ ☆ ☆ ☆ ☆

1=Green
2=Brown
3=Red
4=Pink
5=Yellow

ON THE LOOKOUT.

WHAT COULD BE
IN THE BASKET?

24 CORRECT KING PIG

Which image of King Pig is different? Circle the correct answer.

See Answers

THE ONLY MISSION: PROTECT THE EGGS!

ANSWERS

1

2

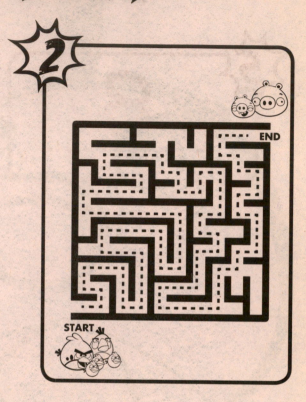

START

END

3

4

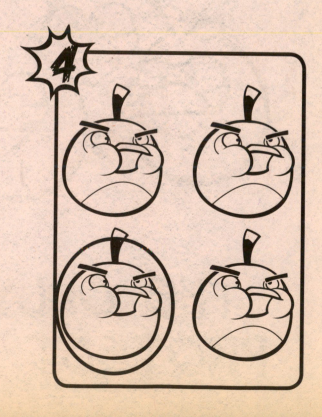

ANSWERS

5

8

6

Possible answers are: eat, father, hat, feet, heat, seat, sat, her

7

18

8

ANSWERS

10

Possible answers are:

word, nerd, heard, third

11

13

3

15

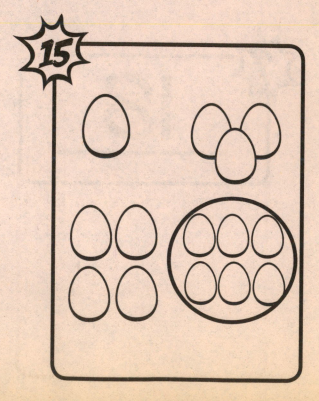

ANSWERS

16

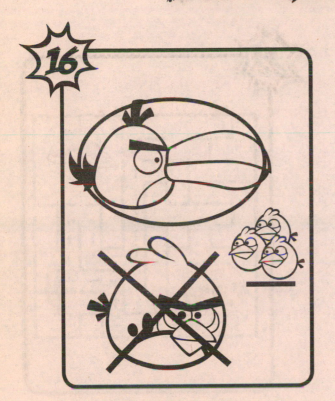

18

19

```
S V E G G S X N I O Y L
B S W V N O P R L G R H
X U L Z C A P G G E O K
T E E I K Z I F B T N N
I N L U N H T D Q F C O
K A T C P G U Y F X I C
P E M R U N S M E S V K
I O B C N C A H L N T O
G N V X M K D S O U X U
S S D R I B D O R T E T
```

20

Possible
answers are:

big, dig, twig,
jig, wig, gig

ANSWERS

21

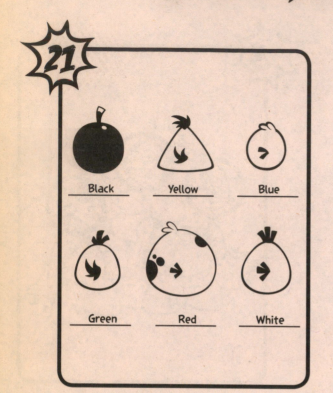

Black Yellow Blue

Green Red White

22

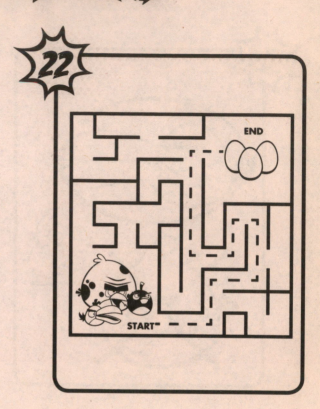

END

START

25